EDG

TABLE OF CONTENTS

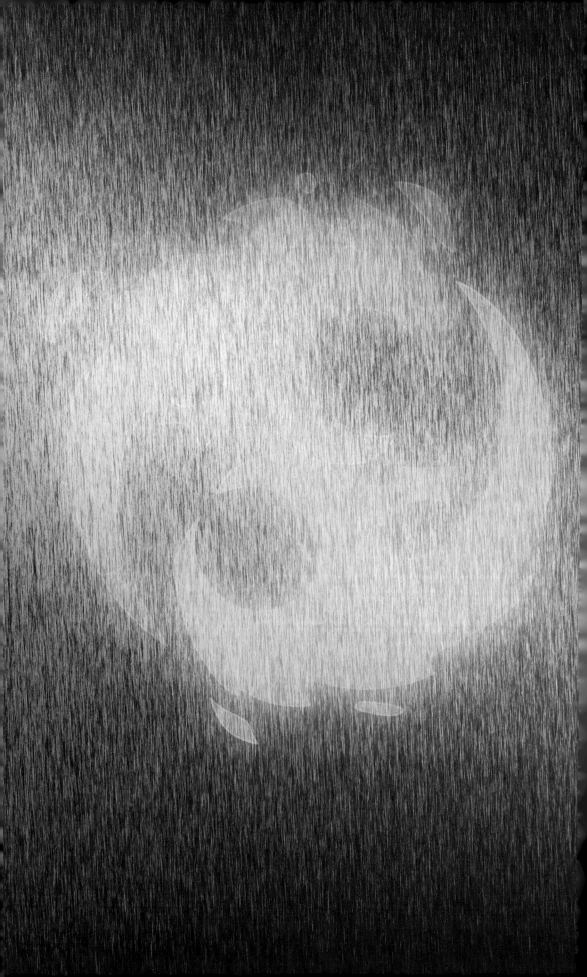

SIGIL™

CHAPTER 21

OUR STORY SO FAR...

SAM

ROIYA

JeMERIK

ZANNIATI

TCHLUSARUD

KHYRADON

FOR CENTURIES, the five human worlds of the Planetary Union have been at war with the lizardlike Saurians of Tcharun, unable to find a weapon formidable enough to turn the tide of battle.

And then along came Sam.

A mustered-out soldier with a good heart, SAMANDAHL REY and his fellow ex-soldier ROIYA SINTOR came looking for work on the neutral world Tanipal only to be ambushed by Sam's Saurian enemy TCHLUSARUD. In the ensuing battle, they picked up two crucial allies – the mysterious JeMERIK MEER (smitten by Roiya) and ZANNIATI (a spy anxious to escape the harem of Tanipal's Sultan). Victory, though, came not from any of them but rather from a strange sigil, a brand of vast power burned into Sam's chest by a vanishing stranger. In fact, Sam first realized the sigil's potential the moment Roiya was slain – and Sam, in a moment of anguished grief, neutralized the attack by unintentionally unleashing a half-mile wide explosion of matter-transforming force.

Once Sam, JeMerik and Zanni escaped Tanipal, however, an over-wrought Sam learned that all was not lost; while Roiya's lifeless body lay in stasis aboard Sam's starship, the *BitterLuck*, her mind and soul had been "uploaded" into the ship's computers seconds before her death, allowing Roiya to live on in holographic form. Now the two of them are taking point in defending the human race from the merciless Saurian army, with Sam on one side as the Planetary Union Field Commander and Khyradon, a self-styled wargod, leading the Saurians in an all-out attack on the Union.

PREVIOUSLY...

His sigil clashing with the energies of the godlike Yala, Sam was inadvertently teleported to distant worlds where he met and fought at the side of fellow Sigil-Bearers Brath Mac Garen and Sephie of Meridian before disappearing again. Meanwhile, Sam's allies are trying – and failing – to protect the Union in Sam's absence. Roiya and JeMerik have returned soldiers from a Saurian prison camp to Gaia; Tchlusarud searches the Saurian homeworld fruitlessly for a key to victory; and Zanni's underground bunker has been attacked by Ronolo's forces...

Chuck DIXON WRITER   **Scot EATON** PENCILER   **Andrew HENNESSY** INKER   **Wil QUINTANA** COLORIST   **Dave LANPHEAR** LETTERER

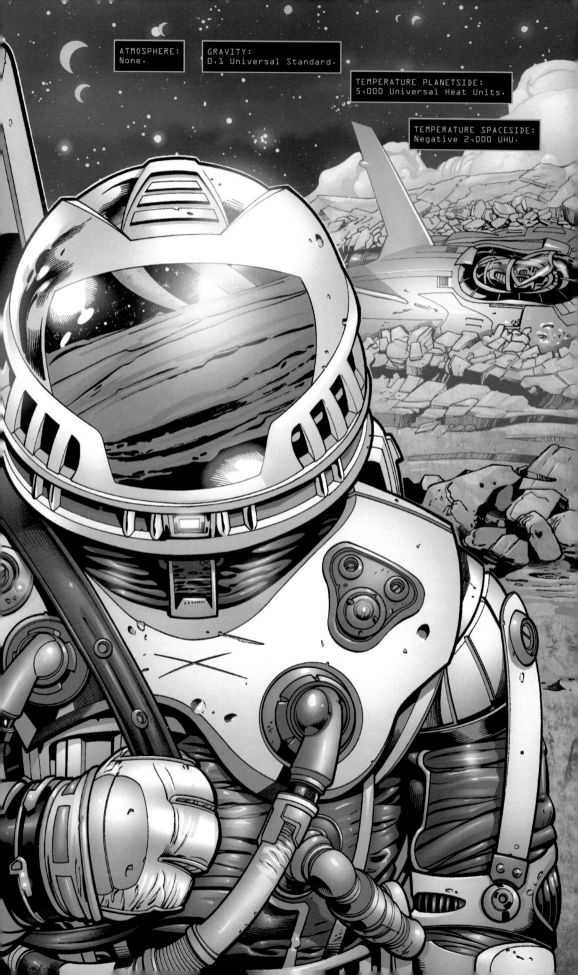

THIS IS *STUPID*. I SEE NO INTRUDER.

YOU WOULD COUNTERMAND GENERAL HRAD ORDER?

SCANNERS SHOW *NOTHING*. A *POINTLESS* ERRAND.

USE YOUR EYES. SCANNERS ARE ONLY *MACHINES*.

NOTHING TO *SEE*. ONLY SOME DUST BLOWING BY ON THE WIND.

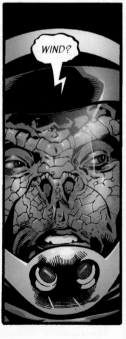

WIND?

ZANNI...

CHOOM
CHOOM
CHOO

SAMANDAHL REY *VANISHES!*

WE HAVE SLAIN THEIR *PATRIARCH.* IT IS *ENOUGH.*

SIGIL™

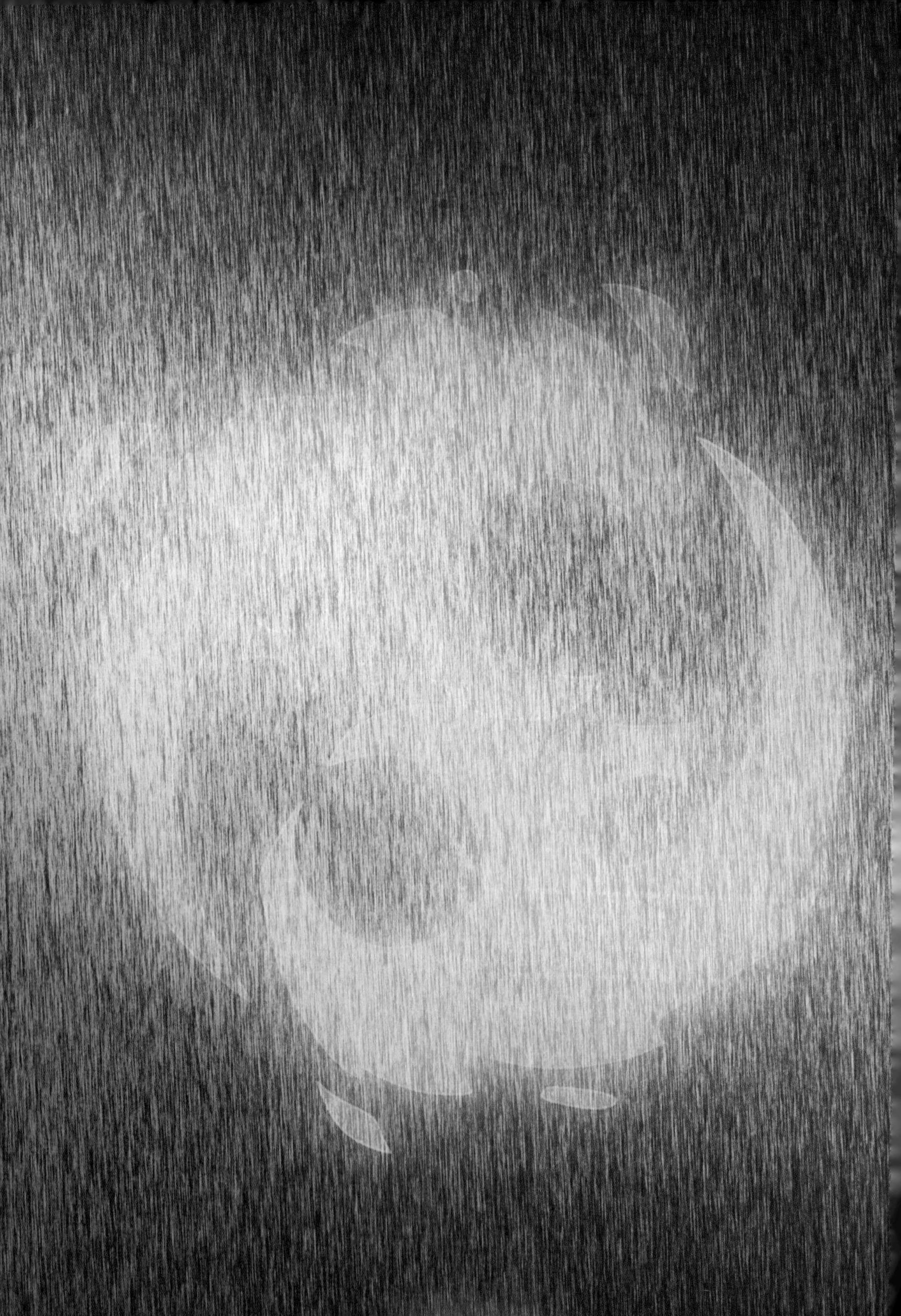

CHAPTER 22
BY

DIXON
Chuck
WRITER

EATON
Scot
PENCILER

HENNESSEY
Andrew
INKER

QUINTANA
Wil
COLORIST

LANPHEAR
Dave
LETTERER

LOVELY ZANNI...

...HOW I WISH WE COULD HAVE GOTTEN ALONG BETTER.

RONOLO?

I HAD TO LEAVE IN A BIT OF A *RUSH*, ZANNI. NO *TIME* FOR SWEET FAREWELLS.

WHERE *IS* EVERYONE, RONOLO?

GENERAL HRAD WANTED TO *TORTURE* YOU. *DESPITE* THE RANCOR BETWEEN US, I COULD NOT BEAR THAT.

YOUR DEATH WILL BE A *QUICK* ONE, MY DEAREST.

I OWE YOU *THAT* MUCH.

"YOU *KNOW* THE KIND OF TROUBLE SHE CAN GET HERSELF INTO."

HIDING DOWN *HERE* WON'T SAVE YOU, DEAR ONE.

I'M *NOT* HIDING, YOU ARROGANT...

THERE MUST BE A WAY TO *STOP* THESE ENGINES.

ARE YOU AWARE THAT AMONG ALL MY WIVES YOU WERE ALWAYS MY *FAVORITE?*

THERE *MUST* BE A WAY...

I SUPPOSE I SHOULD HAVE TOLD YOU... OUR RELATIONSHIP MIGHT NOT BE SO COLD NOW.

THAT WOULD BE TRUE IF YOU DIDN'T...

...*DISGUST* ME!

IN THE BEGINNING...

The First were the creators of the universe before their descent into a constant state of war. Their leader Altwaal ended the war with the creation of the Eidolon rift, a tear in reality which separated their home, Elysia, into two Houses connected by a single gate. Peace and boredom followed. Now the First have been catalyzed into action with the appearance of the Sigil-Bearers, beings of great power that rivals theirs. A Sigil-Bearer has even dared to kill one of their kind. If these Sigil-Bearers can destroy the First, are the First truly gods?

HOUSE SINISTER  HOUSE DEXTER

INGRA
the SEETHING BEAUTY

ORIUM
the ORACLE

GANNISH
the SUFFERER

PERSHA
the UNIFIER

House Sinister's Leader, **Ingra**, is currently scheming to take over House Dexter and reunite the Houses under her rule. Her daughter (by Pyrem) **Persha** seeks out Altwaal, the first Leader of all First, hoping to convince him to return and reunite the Houses. **Pyrem** tries to keep the peace in House Dexter, complicated by an insurrection of the Secundae (naturally-born children of the First) led by **Seahn**, who has made an ally of Ingra. Pyrem has determined that he must sacrifice Seahn and has retrieved one of the legendary seven weapons of Altwaal for that purpose. He is secretly observed by mad **Orium. Gannish** puzzles over his discovery (shared with Persha and his lover **Yala**) that the Atlanteans of Earth are older than the First — but didn't the First create everything else? And **Trenin** grates as Seahn — whom he brought to Elysia as a boy — challenges Pyrem before Dexter's High Council. Pyrem and his would-be replacement agree to meet in the Eidolon...

PYREM
the DIPLOMAT

TRENIN
the HUNTER

YALA
the WARRIOR WOMAN

SEAHN
the DISSIDENT

Barbara
KESEL
WRITER

Andrea
DI VITO
PENCILER

Rob
HUNTER
INKER

Rob
SCHWAGER
COLORIST

Dave
LANPHEAR
LETTERER

YOU ARE *NOT* KERSPAN, PERSHA.

HE WAS INDULGING HIS OWN WOUNDED PRIDE.

YOU ARE SAVING US ALL.

YOU AND INGRA, THAT'S FOOLISH. YOU THINKING SHE CARES ONLY FOR YOU, THAT'S FOOLISH. PLANNING TO COME OUT OF THIS AT HER SIDE, THAT'S FOOLISH.

SO US NOT TELLING HER WE'D MADE ARRANGEMENTS TO CAPTURE PYREM WAS FOOLISH?

NO, THAT WAS *STUPID*, BUT THAT'S GENERALLY HOW I END UP LOOKING WHEN INGRA'S INVOLVED.

NOT AFTER *THIS!*

I *KNOW* DEXTER'S FORCES! THEY'LL SEND AN *ARMY*--EVERYONE--THAT'S WHAT I'D DO!

THIS WILL BE THE *GREATEST* BATTLE IN THE HISTORY OF THE FIRST AND IT WILL CHANGE *EVERY-THING!*

THE *SECUNDAE* WILL *RISE!* *EQUALITY* WILL BE OURS!

AS ONE WHO'S OLD ENOUGH TO REMEMBER THE WARS-- --REIN IT IN, SEAHN. YOU'LL *NEED* THAT ENERGY.

LOOK AT HIM! SEAHN'S SO...EAGER!

THIS ISN'T CHALLENGING THE OLD WAYS-- THIS IS *SELLING OUT* HOUSE DEXTER!

I CAN'T DO THIS. LET'S GO.

ABANDON *SEAHN,* GRACOS?

RAVACA, HE'S ABANDONED US ALREADY.

BUT, *VIHAM--!*

SHHH.

WE HAVE TO FIND THE GATE AND CROSS THE EIDOLON WITH WHAT LITTLE POWER WE HAVE LEFT-- --*WITHOUT* ATTRACTING ATTENTION.

SEAHN. I'M SORRY. TO HAVE YOUR FRIENDS DESERT YOU IN YOUR GREATEST HOUR MUST--

WHAT, ENSON--?

DESER-- *WHAT?*

CHAPTER 5

The PENNY ARCADIAN

Copiously Illustrated   Afternoon Edition, Price One Penny

DOLLYMOP SLAYER STRIKES ANEW

❧ OUR PLAYERS ❧

SIMON ARCHARD
THE CITY'S FAVORITE SON,
HIS MIND IS RAZOR-SHARP

EMMA BISHOP
A FETCHING BEAUTY,
HER SPIRIT CRAVES ADVENTURE

PETER GRIMES
IN PAST A PUGILIST,
UP-AND-COMING GENTLEMAN

EVENING'S LADIES JUSTLY FEARFUL

LATEST VICTIM DISCOVERED

WHERE IS ARCHARD?

During the early hours of yesterday morning another murder of a most revolting and fiendish character took place in the Strunkfield district. This is the fourth which has occurred in this immediate neighbourhood in as many nights, and the character of the mutilations leaves very little doubt that the murderer in this instance is the same person who has committed the previous ones, with which the public are fully acquainted. Ordinarily, the solutions to such crimes are the purview of the inestimable Simon Archard, but his strange yet apparent absence from the investigation is sharply felt, leaving the womenfolk of Partington feel-

ing keenly vulnerable.

At a quarter to 4 o'clock Police-constabl Wharton, 97J, when in Dock's-row, Strunkfield, came upon the body of a woman lying on a part of the footway, and on stooping to raise her up in the belief that she wa drunk he discovered that her throat was cu almost from ear to ear. She was dead bu still warm. A nearby physician rouste from slumber inspected the body at th place where it was found and pronounce the woman dead.

The series of shocking crimes perpetrated is something so distinctly outside the oz dinary range of human experience that has created a kind of stupor extending fa beyond the district where the murders wer committed. One may search the ghastlie efforts of fiction and fail to find anything t surpass these crimes in diabolical audacity

•••PLEASE CONTINUE INSID

Mark **WAID**
WRITER

Butch **GUICE**
PENCILER

Michael **PERKINS**
INKER

Laura **DePUY**
COLORIST

Dave **LANPHEAR**
LETTERER

Copiously Illustrated

The PENN...

Afternoon...

GOLLYMOP SLAYER ...ANEW

EIGHT DAYS.

THAT'S HOW LONG SIMON'S BEEN *GONE* FOR REASONS *MYSTERIOUS* TO PARTS *UNKNOWN*...

...AND THAT'S HOW LONG I'VE BEEN MAINTAINING THE *PRETENSE* THAT HE'S STILL IN *PARTINGTON*.

AS LOATH AS I AM TO *ADMIT* IT...AFTER ALL, THE MAN'S EGO IS ALREADY THE BIGGEST THING IN THE CITY...THE *ACTIVE PRESENCE* OF THE *WORLD'S GREATEST DETECTIVE* IS PERHAPS PARTINGTON'S SINGLE GREATEST *CRIME DETERRENT*.

THE *CHARADE* IS *WEARING* ON ME...BUT THE *LONG-REBUFFED* EMBRACE OF *MORPHEUS* OFFERS NO *REST.* THE MOMENT MY EYES *CLOSE,* MY *WORRIES* TAKE THE FORM OF *NIGHTMARES.* I AM BESET BY VISIONS OF THE *GROTESQUE*...HOT, PANTING BEASTS OF *INDESCRIBABLE HORROR.*

IN MY DELIRIUM, I THINK THEY ARE THE UGLIEST THINGS I HAVE EVER *SEEN.*

I AM *MISTAKEN.*

SAY *HI,* CHESTER!

HI! AAAATABOY. HI!

BURF

SIMON ARCHARD PUT PROFESSIONAL FIGHTER PETER GRIMES TO WORK FOLLOWING SIMON'S EXPOSE OF THE PARTINGTON BOXING SYNDICATE.

PETE'S TESTIMONY WAS INVALUABLE, BUT IT COST HIM HIS CAREER -- SO SIMON TOOK IT UPON HIMSELF TO MAKE PETE NOT ONLY AN AGENT...

...BUT A GENTLEMAN. UNFORTUNATELY FOR PETE...

≥HARRUMPH≤

HOW-DO-YOU-DO-MIS-SUS-SOM-MERS-BY?

...SIMON'S IDEA OF A GENTLEMAN.

POOR PETE. HE FEELS ABOUT AS COMFORTABLE IN A STARCHED COLLAR AS I WOULD DRESSED AS A WHOOPING CRANE.

GOOD EVENING, MR. SOMMERSBY. SAY HELLO, PETER.

HOW-DO-YOU-DO-MIS-TER-SOM-MERS-BY?

STILL, HE PLAYS THE ROLE SIMON SET FOR HIM OUT OF COMPLETE LOYALTY.

I THOUGHT TO BRING PETE ALONG IN CASE I RAN INTO ANY TROUBLE, BUT I AM INSTEAD MET WITH UTTER COURTESY BY CASSIE'S PARENTS...THE FIFTH-GENERATION SOCIAL CENTER OF MUCH OF PARTINGTON'S HIGH SOCIETY.

EVEN USING SIMON'S NAME, THIS WASN'T AN EASY APPOINTMENT TO MAKE. THE SOMMERSBYS, LEGENDARILY PRIVATE TO BEGIN WITH, WERE UNDERSTANDABLY RELUCTANT TO REVISIT THEIR HEARTACHE.

WE CAN'T AFFORD TO RUFFLE ANY FEATHERS HERE UNTIL I LEARN EVERYTHING I--

≥SNIFF≤
≥SNIFF≤

MY WORD! DOES ANYONE ELSE --

WHAT IS THAT DREADFUL SMELL?

PFFT. LOOKA THERE. MUSTA STEPPED IN SOME HORSE PIE OUTSIDE.

LEMME JUST GET THAT...

EEEEEK!

-- CAN.

MY BEST LINEN NAPKINS!

I DUNNO 'BOUT BEST ANYMORE. SORRY. DON'T GET YER BUSTLE IN A KNOT -- I'LL GET RID OF IT.

NOTHING.

TEN O'CLOCK. ELEVEN. TWELVE. ONE.

FOUR HOURS, AND NOT ONE NIBBLE.

A TERM I USE STRICTLY IN THE *FISHING* SENSE, BY THE WAY. NOT THAT I'M PARTICULARLY *EAGER* TO BE TAKEN SERIOUSLY AS SOME *TOFFER*...

...BUT... I MEAN... IS IT *ME*?

AM I DOING SOMETHING *WRONG*, OR--

OH.

THEN AGAIN, I'M *ONE GIRL* ON *ONE NIGHT.* WHAT ARE THE ODDS THAT THE KILLER WILL APPROACH *ME* JUST BECAUSE I *WANT* HIM TO?

UNSURE OF MYSELF, I WALK *AROUND* A BIT TO MAKE MYSELF A *MOVING TARGET...*

...TRYING TO REMEMBER OVER THE OLFACTORY PACKET OF *LAVENDER TOILET WATER* THE SCENT OF DAVID'S *COLOGNE.*

DAVID. I CAN'T REMEMBER THE LAST TIME A MAN LOOKED AT ME AS HE HAS. LET'S JUST HOPE HE NEVER SEES ME LIKE *THIS.*

THE ONLY THING *WORSE* THAN THAT WOULD BE *SIMON* SUDDENLY MATERIALIZING AROUND THE CORNER...

...AN EVENTUALITY EVOKED BY THE FEELING THAT I TRULY *AM* BEING *WATCHED.*

NO EVIDENCE OF SAME, HOWEVER. NO *FOOTPRINTS,* EVEN. JUST THE TRASH AND DETRITUS OF A *TYPICAL URBAN ALLEYWAY.*

...PETE! PETE, *STOP!*

PETE, WE *TALKED* ABOUT THIS! WE HAVE TO LET CUSTOMERS APPROACH OR IT'LL LOOK *SUSPICIOUS!*

I KNOW, BUT...WELL...THE WAY THESE GUYS *LOOK* AT YA...IT'S...THEY'RE...

...I JUST CAN'T *HELP* IT, MISS EMMA.

SIGH.

AND HE HONESTLY *CAN'T.* WHEN WE SAY SOMEONE'S LOYAL TO A *FAULT,* THIS IS *PRECISELY* WHAT WE MEAN. NO, IF WE'RE TO STAND *ANY* CHANCE OF *SNARING* OUR *PREDATOR...*

...WE'LL NEED A *NEW APPROACH.*

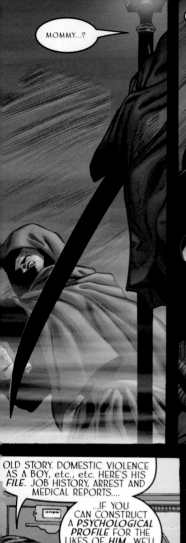

MOMMY...?

MOMMY...?

PUT THE BELT DOWN, MOMMY!

SOMEBODY SAY "BELT"?

FWAM

OLD STORY. DOMESTIC VIOLENCE AS A BOY, etc., etc. HERE'S HIS *FILE*. JOB HISTORY, ARREST AND MEDICAL REPORTS....

...IF YOU CAN CONSTRUCT A *PSYCHOLOGICAL PROFILE* FOR THE LIKES OF *HIM*, WE'LL START MEASURING *YOU* FOR A JACKET.

IT WOULDN'T TAKE *MUCH*.

DESPITE THE INSPECTOR'S *SNIDE CRACK*, WHITSON IS *TEXTBOOK*. EVERYTHING HERE *POINTS* TO SOMEONE WHO'D...

...

OH MY GOD.

IN THE NEXT HALF-HOUR, MY THOUGHTS ARE LED DOWN AN ENTIRELY *NEW*... AND VERY *DARK*...AVENUE. WHERE IS...

ALL RIGHT. ALL RIGHT. THEN WE START FROM *SCRATCH*. WHO HAS *MOTIVE*? A *CO-WORKER*? AN ANGRY *PARENT*? LET'S GO SPEAK WITH HER *FAMILY* AGAIN.

CASSIE WASN'T SIMPLY *PROMISCUOUS*, DAVID.

NO. THE PATTERN WAS ALWAYS THE *SAME*: CASSIE, RESENTFUL OF HER PARENTS' *CONTROLLING NATURE*, WOULD DRAW A LOVER INTO A *SECRET AFFAIR* UNTIL HE *BORED* HER--

--THEN *END* THE RELATIONSHIP AND CONFESS THE DIRTY DETAIL TO HER *FATHER* JUST TO *SPITE* HIM.

I DON'T THINK SOMMERSBY FORCED HER EX-LOVERS OUT OF *PARTINGTON* BECAUSE HE *DISAPPROVED* OF THEM. HE DID IT SO THEY COULDN'T *SPREAD* CASSIE'S DISGRACEFUL SECRET. HIS ENTIRE *SOCIAL STATION* HINGED ON THEIR *SILENCE*.

ALREADY *DONE*.

I REMEMBERED HOW *DISMISSIVE* THEY WERE OF HER *EX-BOYFRIENDS* AND ASKED MYSELF: SUPPOSE THERE WERE MORE *TO* THAT? OUR *SECOND* CONVERSATION FORCED MUCH OF *THIS* OUT IN THE OPEN:

SHE WAS, IN FACT, A *NYMPHOMANIAC*. A *SEX ADDICT*. AND A RATHER *RAUNCHY* ONE, AT *THAT*-- SOMETHING HER UPPER-CRUST PARENTS WORKED *HARD* TO KEEP *SECRET*.

YOU'RE *JOKING*.

HE'S BEEN *CAUGHT*.

IT *HAD* TO BE ONE OF THE FEW OFFICERS WHO KNEW ABOUT THE *SPECIAL BLADE* WHITSON USED...BUT *ALL* OF THEM HAVE *ALIBIS* FOR THAT *NIGHT*. IF YOU'LL *RECALL*, YOU *YOURSELF* TOLD ME WHERE *YOU* WERE.

YOU WERE *THE FIRST ON THE SCENE OF THE MURDER*.

DAVID...

...YOU'RE THE *KILLER*.

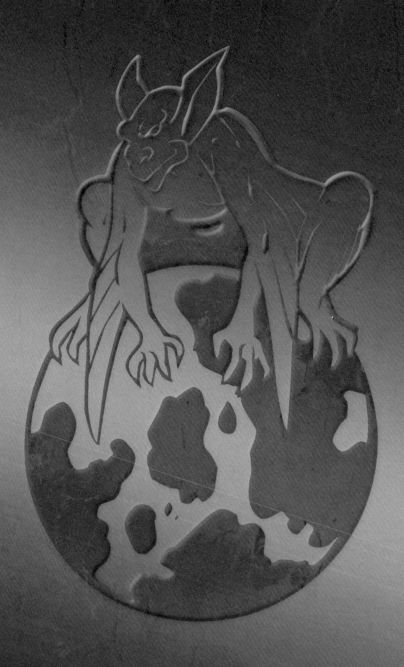

Chapter 6
by

Mark
WAID
WRITER

Jeff
JOHNSON
PENCILER

Paul
NEARY
INKER

Jason
LAMBERT
COLORIST

Dave
LANPHEAR
LETTERER

FEAR **NOT** YOUR **TRAPPINGS**, KIND SIR! YOU SHAN'T FEEL A **THING!**

OF COURSE, THEY SAY THE SAME OF THE GUILLOTINE...

AND WITH THE MAGIC WORDS **SIM SAM RAGATAM** -- NOW YOU **SEE** HIM --

HAHAHAHAHA

AND NOW, LADIES AND GENTLEMEN, THE **CLIMAX** OF TONIGHT'S PERFORMANCE!

YES, I **KNOW** WHAT YOU'RE THINKING! MANY A PERFORMER **BEFORE** CORRADINO HAS FACED *the* **HYDROCOFFIN!** A **FEW** OF THEM -- A **VERY** FEW --

-- HAVE EVEN **SURVIVED!**

BUT TONIGHT YOU WILL STAND **WITNESS** TO THE FACT THAT ONLY **CORRADINO** THE **MAGNIFICENT**

-- CAN ESCAPE FROM ITS GRIP OF **DEATH** WHILE BLIND-FOLDED

-- CORRADINO? YOU MEAN HE DROWNED AN *INNOCENT STRANGER* CHOSEN AT *RANDOM?*

IMAGINE. ONLY *TEN WORDS* IN THAT SENTENCE, AND YET *THREE* OF THEM ARE *WRONG.*

THE *VICTIM* -- HARDLY *"INNOCENT"* -- IS A DETECTIVE WITH THE *BEETON AGENCY.* IT ISN'T COMMON *KNOWLEDGE,* BUT THEY WEAR SPECIAL *SIGNET RINGS* SO AS TO QUIETLY *IDENTIFY* THEMSELVES TO ONE ANOTHER.

WORKING THIS FAR OUT OF *TOWN,* HE MUST HAVE BEEN *TRAILING* SOMEONE -- LIKELY CORRADINO *HIMSELF,* JUDGING BY THE *CIRCUMSTANCES* -- WHICH MEANS HE WAS *HARDLY* CHOSEN AT *"RANDOM."* KILLING HIM PUT AN *END* TO HIS *INVESTIGATION.*

SIMON? *SIMON!*

HMM? OH. YES.

EMMA, PHONE THAT HOTEL *IMMEDIATELY.*

AND...?

AND ASK IF WE'VE TIME TO STOP CORRADINO'S *SECOND* MURDER.

SIMON, HOW DID YOU *KNOW*...? THE *FIRST* VICTIM'S FINGERS SHOWED NO *NICOTINE STAINS*... YET HE'D PURCHASED TOBACCO AND CIGARETTE PAPERS FOR *SOMEONE*, PRESUMABLY A *TRAVELING COMPANION*...AND THE *BEETON* OPERATIVES TRAVEL IN *PAIRS*.

GIVEN THAT FAR MORE *MEN* THAN *WOMEN* ENGAGE IN THE NASTY HABIT OF ROLLING *CIGARETTES*, ODDS WERE THAT COMPANION WAS HIS *INVESTIGATIVE PARTNER* -- AND THUS ANOTHER *TARGET*.

SINCE CORRADINO COULDN'T COMMIT *BOTH* MURDERS ON *STAGE*, HE ARRANGED FOR THE *POISON*...NO DOUBT ONE OF *MANY* CONTINGENCIES...

...THEN STOLE THE FIRST VICTIM'S *IDENTIFICATION* HOPING TO *STALL* ME...

...GIVING THIS MAN TIME TO *DIE*.

> **William Corradine**
> a.k.a. "The Astounding Corradino"
>
> Link suspected between suspect's **touring dates** and mysterious robberies committed **dates** same. Keep Cor...

BUT HOW COULD CORRADINO *POSSIBLY* SURMISE ONLY *ONE* OF THEM WOULD COME TO HIS *SHOW*?

SIMON, WE *ALSO* RECEIVED V.I.P. TICKETS. WHAT *CONCEIVABLE REASON* WOULD CORRADINO HAVE TO INVITE THE WORLD'S *FOREMOST DETECTIVE* TO THE *SCENE* OF HIS *CRIME*?

TO *TAUNT* ME. ALL OF THIS *CONFIRMS* WHAT I'D ALREADY *SUSPECTED*... I AND, APPARENTLY, *MIRANDA CROSS*, WHO GATHERED *NEWSPAPER CLIPPINGS* ON OUR MAGICIAN.

"CORRADINO" IS BUT AN *ALIAS* THE MAN MAINTAINS.

HIS TRUE NAME IS *LIGHTBOURNE*.

ENTER, STAGE LEFT.

THE NIGHT IS *FULL* OF SURPRISES.

MEANING?

WELL, I SEE YOU DON'T WEAR *ANGER* VERY COMFORTABLY.

NOR *YOU* THE ROLE OF *PSYCHOANALYST.* THE *DEDUCTIVE MIND* HAS NO *USE* FOR *ANGER.* THERE-FORE, I AM *NOT ANGRY.*

YOU'RE SOMETHING.

YOU WER *CORREC* ABOUT TH *STAGING*

SIMON, I'M *SERIOUS.* UP UNTIL YOU MENTIONED HIS *NAME,* I'D BELIEVED HIM *DEAD.*

AS HAD *I.*

AND YET YOU'RE *ABSOLUTELY* SURE IT'S *HIM?*

ALMOST. YES, LIKE *CORRADINO,* LIGHTBOURNE WAS A *DEVOTEE* OF *STAGE MAGIC*...BUILDING *TRAPS* AND *GADGETS* WAS HIS *HOBBY*... BUT THAT HARDLY MAKES FOR *CONCLUSIVE IDENTIFICATION.* NO...

...THERE'S ONL ONE WAY TO G *IRREFUTABLE* PROOF...

NO DOUBT THE FIRST MAN RECEIVED A WHISPERED *WARNING* TO PLAY *ALONG* AND STAY *PUT* UNTIL AFTER THE *SHOW*...

...THEN WAS SECRETLY LOWERED THROUGH WHAT'S KNOWN AS A *CAULDRON TRAP*.

I'D *FORGOTTEN*. YOU HAVE SOME *THEATER BACKGROUND*.

DO YOU MISS *PERFORMING*?

WHY? ARE YOU TRYING TO GET *RID* OF ME?

I'M NOT THE *MAGICIAN* HERE.

I SUPPOSE I MISS VENUES LIKE *THIS*. SUPERB *ACOUSTICS*, GAS *FOOTLIGHTS*. SOMETIMES...

...SOMETIMES YOU AND I *BOTH* ALLOW THE PAST TO *ENCROACH* A BIT.

SIMON, *PLEASE* TELL ME MORE ABOUT THIS *"LIGHTBOURNE"* CHARACTER.

HE WAS YOUR FORMER *PARTNER. THAT, I KNOW*...BUT NOT MUCH *MORE*. YOU *NEVER* SPEAK OF HIM.

THEN YOU'RE *USED* TO IT. GOOD.

...AND THAT'S TO *DUPLICATE HIS* FINALE.

SIMON, HAVE YOU LOST YOUR--

HELP ME OR *GO AWAY*. I'M NOT INTERESTED IN *BANTERING*.

...

FINE. BUT TELL ME HOW THIS *HELPS* YOU.

LIGHTBOURNE INVENTED AND SHARED WITH ME CERTAIN *ESCAPE MECHANISMS*... FALSE HINGES, TRICK LOCKS AND THE LIKE.

IF I *RECOGNIZE* THEM AS STEPS IN THE *ESCAPE* PROCEDURE, THEY'RE PRACTICALLY THE *SIGNATURE* TO HIS *CONFESSION*.

AND THE *BLINDFOLD*?

DOES IT SECRETLY CONTAIN ANYTHING THAT WOULD *HELP*?

NO.

THEN *THERE*, I DRAW THE *LINE*.

ONE OF US HAS TO BE *SANE*.

IT OCCURS TO ME THERE ARE LESS *FLAMBOYANT* WAYS TO EXAMINE THIS DEVICE.

EMMA, DO *NOT*--

→SIGH←

MISS *BISHOP*, DO NOT *ARGUE* WITH ME.

CLOSE THE *LID*.

IF YOU SHOW EVIDENCE OF BEING IN *ANY* TROUBLE WHATSO-EVER, I *WILL* BASH THROUGH THE GLASS WITH THAT *AXE*.

YOU WON'T NEED IT.

Y'MEAN HE DUNKED HISSELF IN THERE ON *PURPOSE*?

WORSE. WITH A SORT OF *EAGERNESS.*

THERE WAS ALMOST A...I WANT TO SAY *"COMPETITIVE"* SENSE TO IT, BUT THAT'S *NOT* THE SIMON I...

NEVER MIND. I'VE ALREADY SAID TOO MUCH.

HE'S PROBABLY *RIGHT*. I'VE LITTLE DOUBT HE CAN DO THIS. THAT'S NOT WHAT'S WORRYING ME.

MY *CONCERN* IS THAT SIMON IS ACTING WITH UNCHARACTERISTIC *EMOTION* --

YOU THERE -- GET *AWAY* FROM THAT!

THERE'S BEEN A MAN *MURDERED* HERE AND --

-- *OH!* IT'S *YOU!* BEGGING Y'R *PARDON,* MIZ BISHOP. SO, C'N YER BOSS *EXPLAIN ANY* O'THESE *GOINGS-ON* TO A LOWLY *STAGE MANAGER...?*

WOULD *THAT,* KIND SIR. MR. ARCHARD HAS HIS *LEADS,* BUT HE'S CHOSEN A RATHER *UNCHARACTERISTIC* MANNER IN WHICH TO *PURSUE* THEM.

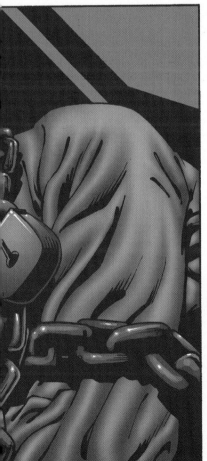

WHATEVER'S RATTLIN' THROUGH 'IS SKULL, IT'S BEYOND YOU 'N' *I,* THAT'S F'SURE. IT'S *HIS SHOW.*

REGULAR FOLKS LIKE *US,* ALL WE C'N DO IS JUST STAND HERE *STAGE RIGHT* 'N' WATCH 'IM *WORK.*

THAT *IS* SOMETIMES THE *CASE* -- THOUGH I CONFESS I'M BEGINNING TO FEEL IT HAPPENING *MORE* AND *M--*

THIS IS STAGE *LEFT*.

LIGHTBOURNE.

SPEAKING.

AND THE *REAL* STAGE MANAGER?

IT'S OVER *HERE.*

THE POOR MAN SIMPLY WENT TO *PIECES.*

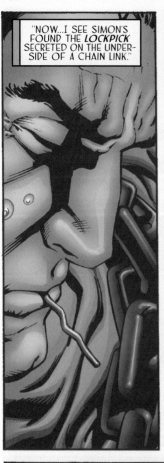

"NOW...I SEE SIMON'S FOUND THE *LOCKPICK* SECRETED ON THE UNDER-SIDE OF A CHAIN LINK."

EXCELLENT.

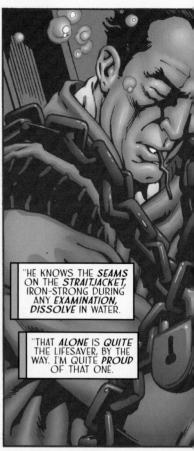

"HE KNOWS THE *SEAMS* ON THE *STRAITJACKET*, IRON-STRONG DURING ANY *EXAMINATION*, *DISSOLVE* IN WATER."

"THAT *ALONE* IS *QUITE* THE LIFESAVER, BY THE WAY. I'M QUITE *PROUD* OF THAT ONE."

"BRAVO, SIMON!"

"NOW THE *FINAL* GIMMICK. SIMON RECALLS THIS ONE, *TOO*. THE *LID* CONTAINS A HIDDEN DOOR THAT CAN PROVIDE *EGRESS*..."

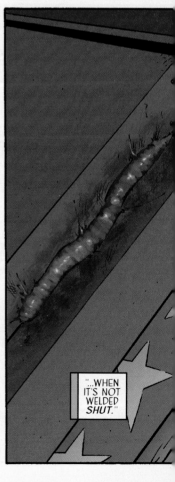

"...WHEN IT'S NOT WELDED *SHUT*."

CHAPTER 20

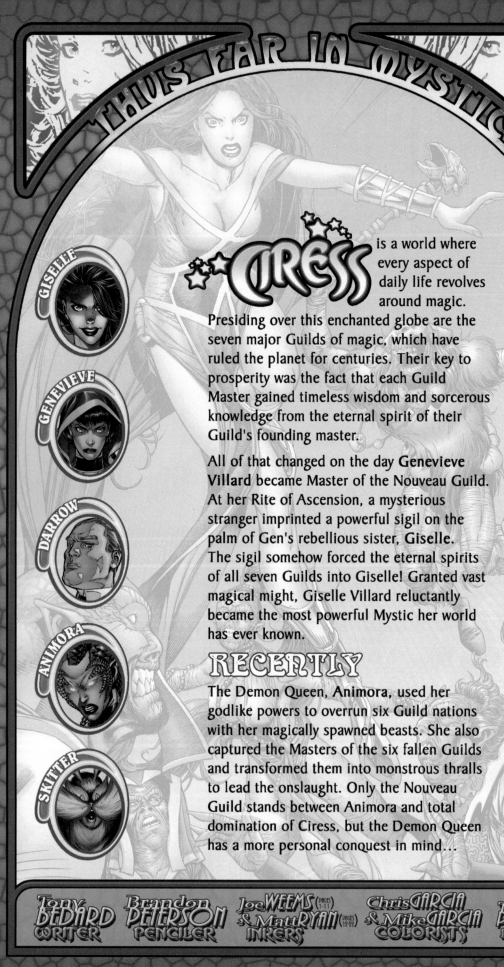

GISELLE

GENEVIEVE

DARROW

ANIMORA

SKITTER

★★CIRESS is a world where every aspect of daily life revolves around magic. Presiding over this enchanted globe are the seven major Guilds of magic, which have ruled the planet for centuries. Their key to prosperity was the fact that each Guild Master gained timeless wisdom and sorcerous knowledge from the eternal spirit of their Guild's founding master.

All of that changed on the day **Genevieve Villard** became Master of the Nouveau Guild. At her Rite of Ascension, a mysterious stranger imprinted a powerful sigil on the palm of Gen's rebellious sister, **Giselle**. The sigil somehow forced the eternal spirits of all seven Guilds into Giselle! Granted vast magical might, Giselle Villard reluctantly became the most powerful Mystic her world has ever known.

RECENTLY

The Demon Queen, Animora, used her godlike powers to overrun six Guild nations with her magically spawned beasts. She also captured the Masters of the six fallen Guilds and transformed them into monstrous thralls to lead the onslaught. Only the Nouveau Guild stands between Animora and total domination of Ciress, but the Demon Queen has a more personal conquest in mind…

Tony **BEDARD** WRITER

Brandon **PETERSON** PENCILER

Joe **WEEMS** (PAGES 1-11) & Matt **RYAN** (PAGES 12-22) INKERS

Chris **GARCIA** & Mike **GARCIA** COLORISTS

Troy **PETERI** LETTERER

...WAIT ...→NGH←... DON'T...!

THEY'VE SWITCHED FROM SPELL-CASTING TO MORE DIRECT PHYSICAL ATTACKS!

GISELLE, YOU CAN'T DEFLECT THESE LIKE THE OTHER—

GISELLE!

BAM

THRUNCH

COLOSSUS FIVE TO NOUVEAU LINE COMMAND! WE'VE TAKEN A HIT!

CALM DOWN, LeCAVALIER. IF THEY'RE GETTING PHYSICAL WITH HER, THEN THEY'VE STRAYED INTO MY TERRITORY.

AND WHAT WOULD THE TANTRIC GUILD SUGGEST?

KISSING THE ENEMY? OR PERHAPS A NICE GROUP HUG?

THE SPELL I HAVE IN MIND WOULD REQUIRE GISELLE TO SHUNT MUCH OF HER POWER INTO A TOUGHER BODY...

SHE CAN *HEAR* US...?!

ANIMORA! HELP US!

SHHHLUK

GENERAL LAURANCE!

MASTER VILLARD.

GENEVIEVE...

I SERVED YOUR *FATHER.* I'VE *KNOWN* YOU AND GISELLE SINCE YOU WERE LITTLE GIRLS. *YOU* TURNED OUT TO BE EVERYTHING I EXPECTED... BUT *TELL* ME...

...WHAT IN THE WORLD HAS YOUR *SISTER* TURNED INTO...?

OUR LAST HOPE.

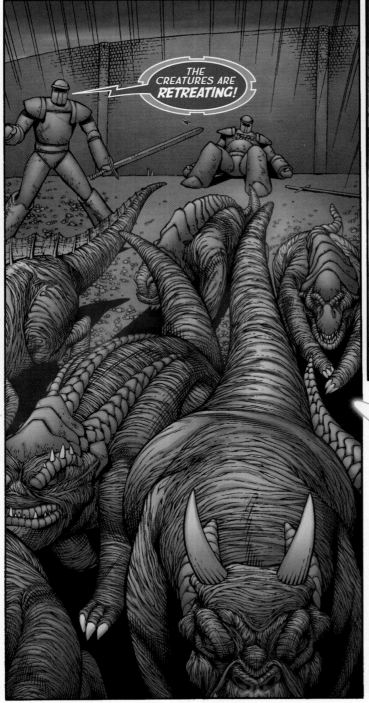

...LOOKS LIKE THEY'RE **CONVERGING** JUST A FEW HUNDRED METERS IN FRONT OF YOUR POSITION, AND...

SHWUP

...SEVEN SPIRITS...

KRUNCH

MUCHA

KLIMT

GLUP

SHLUP

MASTER VILLARD...

I *SEE* IT, JACQUES.

Oh, THAT IS JUST *GROSS*...

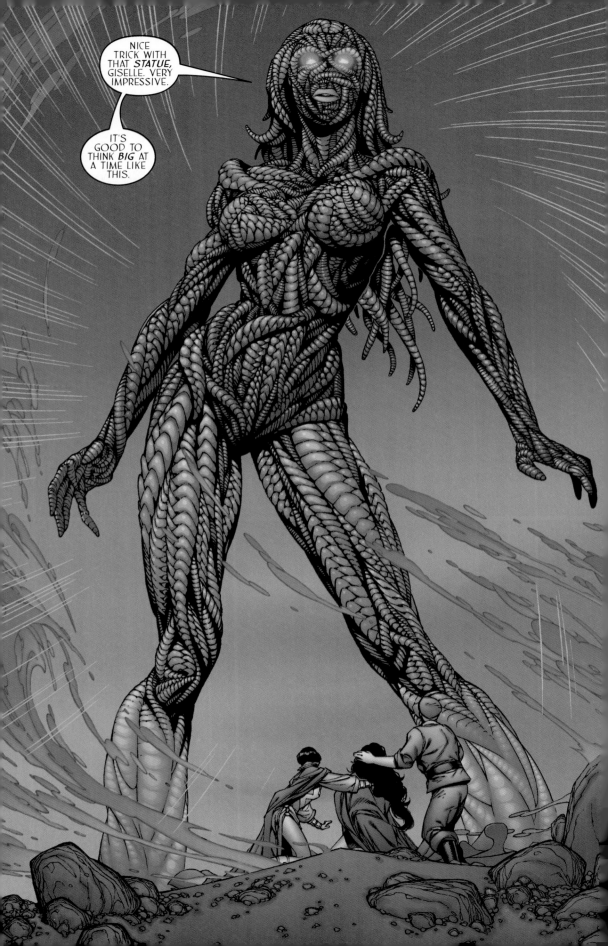

ALL OF THIS...JUST TO GET HERSELF KILLED?

NO... THERE IS ANOTHER CASUALTY HERE...

GISELLE! GET AWAY FROM HER!

...YOU WIN...

...YOU WIN...

...YOU WIN...

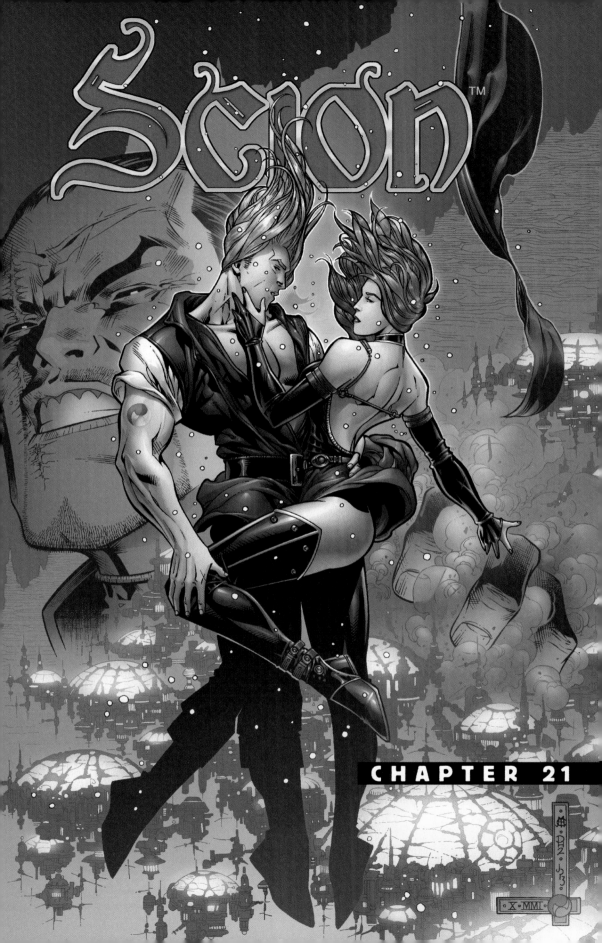

CHAPTER 21

Thus Far in Scion

Ethan

Ashleigh

Skink

Bron

Exeter

Nadia

Mai Shen

What started with a mysterious sigil led to war. Prince Ethan of the West-ruling Heron Dynasty was graced with a mark granting him power, leading to the accidental scarring of Prince Bron of the East-ruling Raven Dynasty during ritual combat.

When the battle was met, first victory belonged to the Herons, but Ethan's oldest brother and heir to the throne, Artor, was brutally slain by Bron. Ethan swore vengeance.

Not long after, Bron was imbued with power by Mai Shen, who revealed herself to him as a member of the godlike First. Bron then murdered his father, framed his sister Ashleigh for the crime, and took the throne for himself.

Ethan confronted Bron in the Raven Keep but was defeated, managing to escape with his life thanks to Ashleigh's help. The Raven princess was, in fact, part of the Underground movement dedicated to freeing the genetically engineered Lesser Races.

Ethan promised his loyalty to the Underground, much to the chagrin of his brother Kai and sister Ylena, who are leading the Heron invasion. Intending to find a new sanctuary for the Lesser Races, Ethan and Ashleigh stole a submersible craft and set off for the undersea city of Haven. Ethan's Lesser Race friends Skink and Exeter, along with a traveler named Nadia, arranged to meet Ethan upon his return.

Meanwhile, Bernd Rechts, a member of the First who had been advising the Heron war effort but was apparently slain by Mai Shen, returned to the Heron encampment. Rechts urged a quick strike at the Raven capital via a dangerous mountain pass.

Ron **marz** WRITER

Jim **cheung** & Brandon peterson PENCILERS

Don **hillsman II** INKER

Justin **ponsor** & Jason lambert COLORISTS

Troy **peter** LETTERER

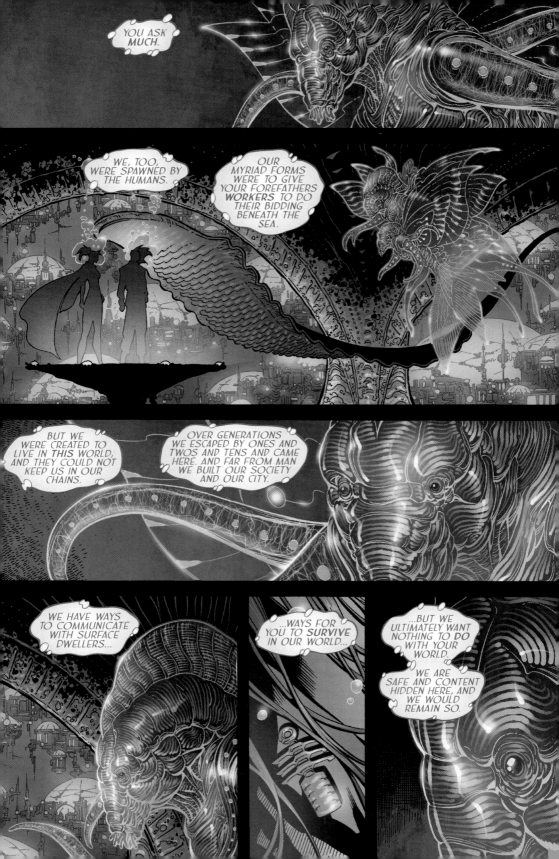

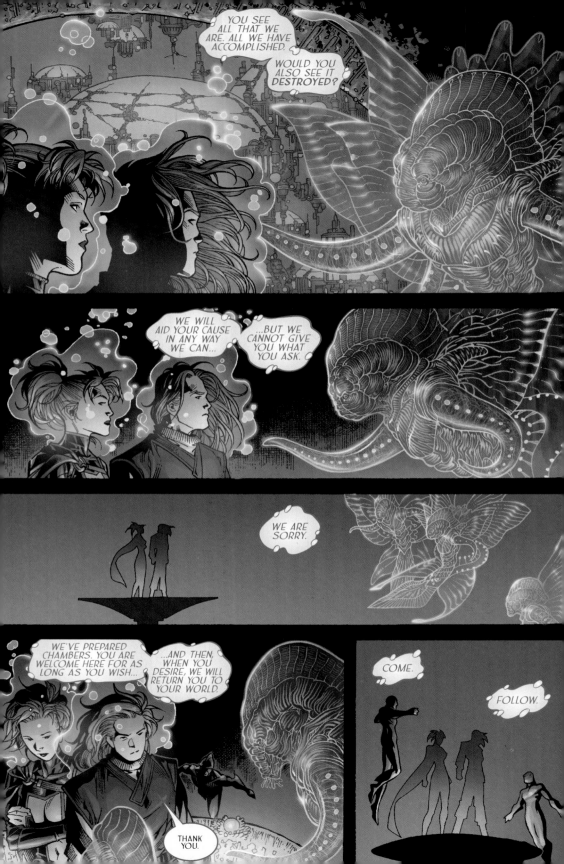

IF THERE IS ANYTHING TO BE SALVAGED FROM YOUR CRAFT, WE WILL BE HAPPY TO RETRIEVE IT FOR YOU.

SHOULD YOU NEED ANY FURTHER COMFORTS, DO NOT HESITATE TO ASK. OTHERWISE...

...WE SHALL RESPECT YOUR PRIVACY.

I'M SORRY, ASHLEIGH.

I REALLY THOUGHT HAVEN WAS THE ANSWER. NOW I CAN SEE THAT WAS...

...NAÏVE.

I'M SORRY I *FAILED* YOU.

ETHAN...

ASHLEIGH, I...

...CARE ABOUT YOU...

...VERY MUCH, BUT I DON'T KNOW HOW WE CAN *EVER* BE TOGETHER. OUR KINGDOMS ARE AT *WAR*, OUR FAMILIES—

Shhh

I TOLD YOU BEFORE...

...ALL WE HAVE IS EACH OTHER.

...SINCE THIS INVASION FORCE IS OUR BEST HOPE OF *ENDING* THE CONFLICT IN OUR FAVOR.

PERHAPS OUR *ONLY* HOPE.

YOU LEAD AN IMPRESSIVE ARMY, PRINCESS YLENA.

I ASSURE YOU, THE END OF THE WAR IS VERY NEAR INDEED.

I'D FEEL A GOOD DEAL MORE CERTAIN OF OUR SUCCESS IF WE HAD ETHAN...

...*AND* HIS POWER...

...AT OUR SIDE.

INSTEAD HE'S OFF WITH THAT RAVEN WITCH OF HIS, PROVING HIS *IDEALISM*.

YES, YOUR BROTHER PURSUES HIS OWN COURSE RATHER THAN THE ONE EXPECTED OF HIM...

...AND YES, HIS ABILITIES WOULD BE A BOON. BUT ETHAN IS NOT A *NECESSITY* TO VICTORY.

PARTICULARLY WHEN OUR SCOUTS STILL DETECT NO SIGN OF RAVEN OPPOSITION.

LET'S HOPE IT *REMAINS* SO UNTIL WE REACH THE CAPITAL.

I DON'T WANT BRON TO KNOW WE'RE ANYWHERE *NEAR* UNTIL WE KNOCK ON HIS DOOR.

Oh, I'M SURE EVERYTHING WILL WORK OUT JUST AS PLANNED.

MOST OF THE HERON FORCE IS IN THE NOTCH NOW...

...THEY'LL BE WITHIN RANGE SOON.

LET THEM COME TO *US*, KORT. THE HOLOGRAM GENERATORS WILL MASK OUR PRESENCE UNTIL IT'S *FAR* TOO LATE.

MAI SHEN HAS BEEN NOTICEABLY ABSENT FROM YOUR SIDE OF LATE, BRON.

SHE'S SUPPOSED TO BE OUR *WAR ADVISOR*, SHOULDN'T SHE AT LEAST BE HERE FOR THE ATTACK?

NOT TO WORRY, DEAR BROTHER...

...SHE'S HERE.

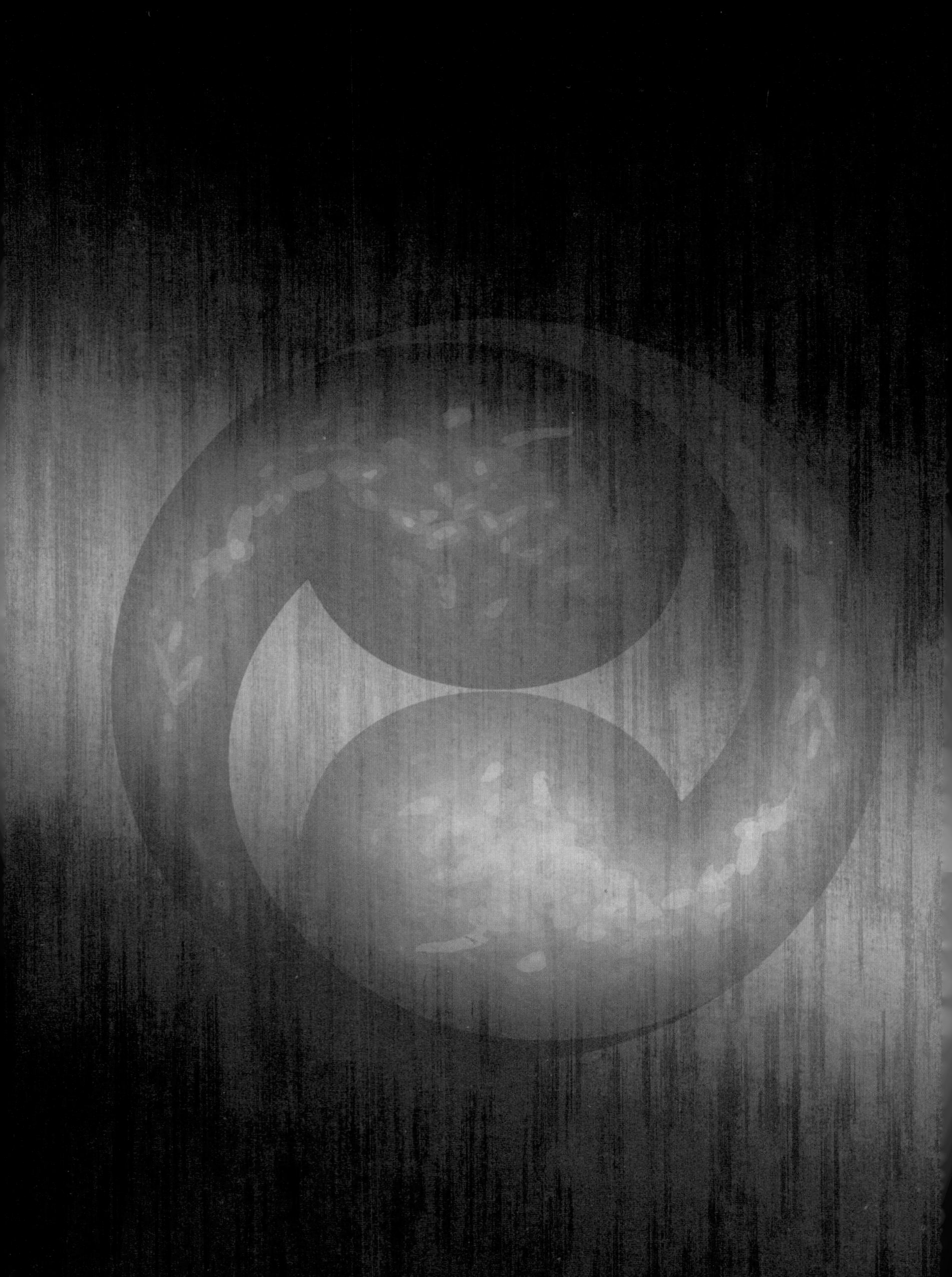

Chapter 22
by

Ron
MARZ
WRITER

Karl
MOLINE
PENCILER

John
DELL
INKER

Matt
MILLA
COLORIST

Troy
PETERI
LETTERER

ETHAN IS THE YOUNGEST PRINCE OF THE HERON DYNASTY.

THE HERONS AND THE RIVAL RAVEN DYNASTY HAVE BEEN ENEMIES FOR AS LONG AS EITHER CAN REMEMBER, THEIR MUTUAL HATRED BOILING OVER INTO A WAR THAT LASTED CENTURIES. FINALLY A TENUOUS PEACE WAS STRUCK, AND OPEN WARFARE WAS REPLACED BY AN ANNUAL TOURNAMENT OF INDIVIDUAL COMBAT.

BUT AT THE MOST RECENT TOURNAMENT, ETHAN VIOLATED THE RULES BY PERMANENTLY SCARRING PRINCE BRON OF THE EAST. THE ACT WASN'T INTENTIONAL. ETHAN'S ARM HAD BEEN MARKED WITH THE SYMBOL YOU SAW, AND HE WAS UNABLE TO CONTROL THE POWER IT GAVE HIM. BUT THE DAMAGE HAD BEEN DONE.

WAR AGAIN FLARED BETWEEN THE HERONS AND THE RAVENS. I KNOW ETHAN STILL FEELS PERSONALLY RESPONSIBLE FOR IT, EVEN THOUGH WHAT TRANSPIRED WAS BEYOND HIS CONTROL. HE HELPED BRING ABOUT VICTORY AT THE FIRST BATTLE...

EXETER?

HE WAS A BOUNTY HUNTER, THE MOST FEARED IN RAVEN OR HERON LANDS. HE'D NEVER FAILED TO BRING IN A MARK...

...UNTIL ETHAN **DEFEATED** HIM AND SHOWED HIM MERCY. EXETER'S SINCE HAD A CHANGE OF HEART AND TAKEN UP THE UNDERGROUND'S CAUSE.

AN INTERESTING CHOICE TO RECRUIT SUPPORT FOR THE UNDERGROUND. I IMAGINE ETHAN THINKS IF OTHERS SEE **EXETER** BELIEVING IN FREEDOM, THEY MIGHT ALLOW **THEMSELVES** TO BELIEVE IN IT AS WELL.

SKINK, THE UNDERGROUND WANTS FREEDOM FOR THE LESSER RACES, YET **YOU'RE** STILL ETHAN'S SERVANT. WHY IS THAT?

ETHAN TREATS ME AS AN **EQUAL.** HE ALWAYS HAS.

I SERVE HIM OUT OF THE OBLIGATION OF **FRIENDSHIP**, NOT **SERVITUDE.**

WHICH IS WHY WE WAIT HERE FOR HIS RETURN.

THERE'S BEEN LITTLE TIME TO GET ACQUAINTED SINCE YOU JOINED US, NADIA. YOU'VE SHARED ALMOST **NOTHING** OF YOURSELF.

YOU'VE ONLY SAID YOU WERE A **TRAVELER.** WHERE DO YOU HAIL FROM?

FAR AWAY.

I WANTED TO SEE WHAT **ELSE** AVALON OFFERED.

NOW I FIND MYSELF IN A LAND TORN BY **WAR.**

THE INVASION CONTINUES EVEN AS WE SIT HERE. ETHAN'S BROTHER AND SISTER LEAD THEIR TROOPS TOWARD THE RAVEN CAPITAL.

THE COMING BATTLE MAY WELL DECIDE THIS WAR'S OUTCOME...

THERE...

...THEY'VE RETURNED.

YOU SEE, SKINK? YOUR CONCERN WAS UNNECESSARY.

ETHAN'S *FINE.*

I KNEW HE *WOULD* BE.

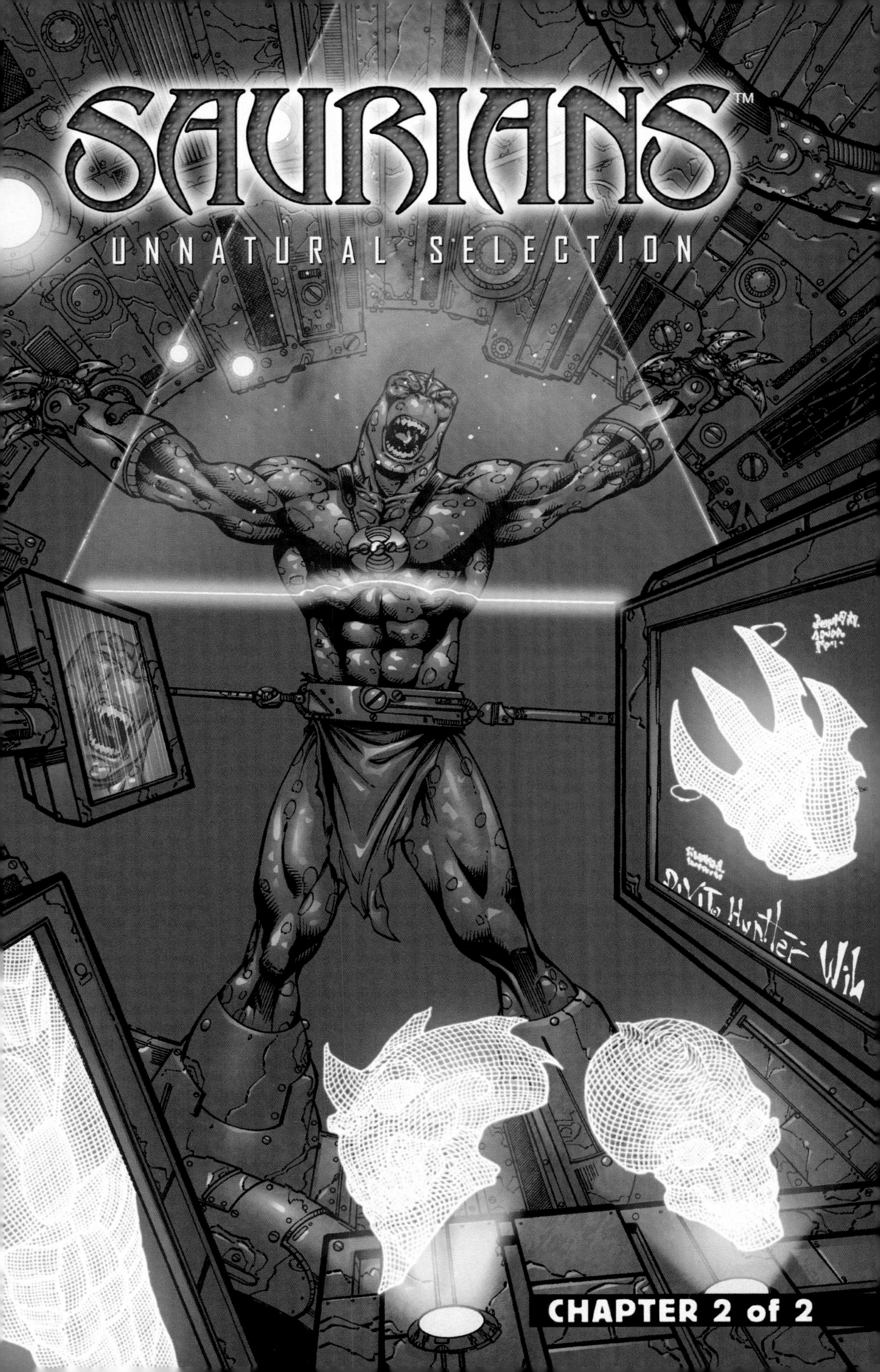
SAURIANS™
UNNATURAL SELECTION
CHAPTER 2 of 2

EVOLUTION'S MASTER!

Over four hundred years ago, the human worlds of the Planetary Union became enmeshed in a war against the lizardlike Saurians of Tcharun. The humans— far more technologically and militarily advanced than the Saurians—were guaranteed victory...

...until a Saurian named Terchac accidentally uncovered a critical secret that put horrifying truth to these words:

You are what you eat...

Mark **WAID** & Tony **BEDARD**
WRITERS

Andrea **DI VITO**
PENCILER

Rob **HUNTER**
INKER

Wil **QUINTANA**
COLORIST

Dave **LANPHEAR** & Troy **PETERI**
LETTERERS

All combat is deception,
Feint and parry, bait and thrust.
Wise are warriors who can find
Rivals worthy of their trust.

The Song of Khyalhtua

AS A NEOPHYTE DIVINITY SCHOLAR, I THOUGHT I KNEW WHAT THAT SCRIPTURE MEANT. THEN CAME THE WAR WITH THE HUMANS...

...AND AFTER I'D FOUGHT THE ENEMY, AFTER I'D TASTED THEIR TREACHERY AND FOUNDED THE CHURCH OF TRANSFORMATION BASED ON THE BITTER LESSONS I'D LEARNED...

...THAT SCRIPTURE MEANT SOMETHING *ELSE* ENTIRELY.

TWO CENTURIES LATER, WHEN THE ANCIENT *ORDER OF KHYALHTUA* SOUGHT TO STAMP OUT MY FLEDGLING CHURCH, ITS MEANING WOULD CHANGE FOR ME YET AGAIN.

BUT THAT'S THE MIRACLE OF THE HOLY WRIT: ITS TRUTH CONTINUES TO *EVOLVE,* EVEN AS *I* DO.

...I HAD COME HOME FROM THE WAR IN SHACKLES-- THE FREAK WHO'D **EATEN** A HUMAN WAS NOW **TURNING INTO** ONE.

MY DESPERATE ACT BROUGHT TO LIGHT AN EVOLUTIONARY ADAPTATION WE HAD LONG FORGOTTEN: OUR ABILITY TO **ABSORB** PHYSICAL TRAITS FROM THE ANIMALS WE CONSUME.

SINCE WE HAD ABSORBED ALL WE NEEDED FROM THE OTHER SPECIES ON TCHARUN EONS AGO, SAURIAN PHYSIOLOGY REMAINED UNCHANGED UNTIL **I** DEVOURED **ALIEN** FLESH.

THE SCIENTISTS COULDN'T GET ENOUGH OF ME. MY CASE WAS A **REVELATION**. THEY SLICED AND SAMPLED ME FOR **YEARS**, EVEN FORCING ME TO CONSUME **MORE** ENEMY FLESH.

IN TIME THEY LEARNED HOW THE INGESTION METAMORPHOSIS WORKED... AND HOW TO **ACCELERATE** THE RESULTS.

IT WAS THEIR LAST-DITCH EFFORT TO ACHIEVE A BALANCE OF POWER IN THE ALL-BUT-LOST WAR AGAINST THE HUMANS. AND IT **WORKED**.

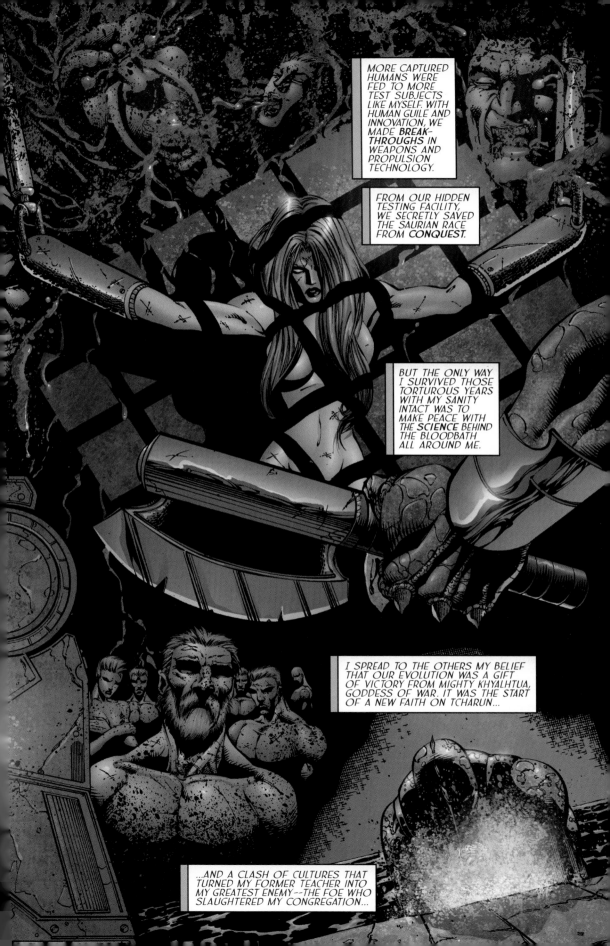

MORE CAPTURED HUMANS WERE FED TO MORE TEST SUBJECTS LIKE MYSELF. WITH HUMAN GUILE AND INNOVATION, WE MADE BREAK-THROUGHS IN WEAPONS AND PROPULSION TECHNOLOGY.

FROM OUR HIDDEN TESTING FACILITY, WE SECRETLY SAVED THE SAURIAN RACE FROM CONQUEST.

BUT THE ONLY WAY I SURVIVED THOSE TORTUROUS YEARS WITH MY SANITY INTACT WAS TO MAKE PEACE WITH THE SCIENCE BEHIND THE BLOODBATH ALL AROUND ME.

I SPREAD TO THE OTHERS MY BELIEF THAT OUR EVOLUTION WAS A GIFT OF VICTORY FROM MIGHTY KHYALHTUA, GODDESS OF WAR. IT WAS THE START OF A NEW FAITH ON TCHARUN...

...AND A CLASH OF CULTURES THAT TURNED MY FORMER TEACHER INTO MY GREATEST ENEMY--THE FOE WHO SLAUGHTERED MY CONGREGATION...

HRUKKAN SPENT THE REST OF THAT FATEFUL DAY VISITING CONTACT AFTER CONTACT, PAINSTAKINGLY FERRETING OUT THE IDENTITY OF WHOEVER HAD ORDERED THE DESTRUCTION OF MY CHURCH.

I COULDN'T KEEP CLOSE ENOUGH TO HEAR EVERYTHING THAT WAS SAID--

--BUT I NEVER LET HIM OUT OF MY SIGHT.

AND, I MUST ADMIT, HAVING THE HIGHEST SPIRITUAL LEADER ON ALL OF TCHARUN AS MY PERSONAL ERRAND-BOY GAVE ME NO END OF SATISFACTION.

IN TIME, HE LEARNED THAT THE FACTION WHICH STRUCK AGAINST ME WAS GATHERING FOR A SECRET MEETING THAT VERY NIGHT.

WE CREPT OUT TO THE APPOINTED PLACE, INTENT ON DESTROYING THOSE WHO HAD SOUGHT TO START A CIVIL WAR. OUR MUTUAL INTERESTS WERE CLEAR ENOUGH THAT I ALLOWED HRUKKAN TO ARM HIMSELF WITH A *ZAKRI*.

IN THE HANDS OF THE WEAPONSMASTER, THE DOUBLE-BLADED WEAPON WAS DEADLIER THAN ANY ORDNANCE WE WERE LIKELY TO FACE.

NEVERTHELESS, I BROUGHT ALONG A *PLASMA RIFLE*, AS FORTUNE RARELY FAVORS THE OVERCONFIDENT.

WE'RE HERE.

OF COURSE I KNEW THIS WOULD BE A SET-UP.

HRUKKAN HAD BEEN TELLING HIS CONTACTS TO CAPTURE MY OWN KEY DISCIPLES AND BRING THEM TO THIS CLEARING...

...SO THAT I COULD BE TRICKED INTO KILLING THEM MYSELF.

INSTEAD, I WENT IN DELIBERATELY AIMING FOR HRUKKAN'S MEN, WHO WERE HIDDEN IN THE TREES.

HRUKKAN'S FURY UNBALANCED HIM. I PASSED UP SEVERAL OPENINGS, ALLOWING HIM TO REGAIN HIS FOCUS.

HE WAS LASHING OUT IN BLIND RAGE, LIKE A WOUNDED BEAST. IT WOULD HAVE BEEN A SIN TO FINISH HIM OFF IN SUCH A SORRY STATE.

EVENTUALLY, I TOOK HRUKKAN'S POST AS WEAPONSMASTER, AND EVEN THE SAURIAN ROYAL FAMILY ADOPTED THE SAME EVOLUTIONARY METHODS THAT I HAD BROUGHT HOME TO TCHARUN.

BUT TWO HUNDRED ORBITS LATER, HRUKKAN'S LAST WORDS OCCASIONALLY RISE TO TAUNT ME.

IF ONLY HE COULD HAVE LIVED TO SEE THE DAY WHEN THE WAR GODDESS HERSELF APPEARED BEFORE ME, AND GRANTED ME MY *FINAL* TRANSFORMATION.

WITH HER HOLY POWER COURSING THROUGH ME, I CUT THE HUMAN SOLDIERS DOWN LIKE GRASS. EVEN MY OLD NAME HAS BEEN CAST ASIDE LIKE A SKIN I'VE OUTGROWN.

WHAT NOW, LORD *KHYRADON?*

OUR WORK HERE IS DONE, CAPTAIN CHARKI. TIME TO CRUSH THEIR NEXT OUTPOST.

WELL... *THIS* BRINGS BACK MEMORIES...

A *FLAMETHROWER.* I USED ONE OF THESE IN MY *FIRST* ENCOUNTER WITH THE HUMANS.

I THOUGHT AT THE TIME THAT IT WAS THE WORST MISTAKE OF MY LIFE, BUT IN FACT IT TAUGHT ME SOMETHING *VITAL...*

"...THE VERY SAME WISDOM I PASSED ON TO WEAPONSMASTER HRUKKAN AS HIS *FINAL LESSON.*"

CAN YOU GUESS WHAT THAT LESSON WAS, CAPTAIN?

KLAK

I HAVE NO NEED TO *GUESS,* LORD KHYRADON. I RECITE IT EVERY TIME I RECEIVE COMMUNION...

"FROM OUR BITTEREST ENEMIES WE SEIZE OUR FINEST WEAPONS."

VERY GOOD, CAPTAIN. LET'S GO MAKE SURE THE REST OF HUMANITY LEARNS IT THE *HARD* WAY.

Discover the
WAY OF THE RAT ™

A new ongoing series joins the EDGE lineup next month in EDGE #5. WAY OF THE RAT is written by Chuck Dixon with pencils by Jeff Johnson, whose 10 year career includes stints on **Spider-Man**, **Wonder Man**, and **Legend of Supreme**.

Inking Jeff is Tom Ryder, who started inking in 1991, but who for the last four years was storyboarding for Sony Animation. Chris Oarr sat down with Johnson and Ryder for an advance look at CrossGen's hot new martial arts series.

OARR: So tell us about WAY OF THE RAT. What's it all about?

JEFF JOHNSON: WAY OF THE RAT is a martial arts adventure set in a world that resembles First or Second Dynasty China Basically, I finally get to draw a kung fu movie. I think most people will recognize the Jackie Chan influence, because I'm a huge fan of his pictures and the genre in general. But the true connoisseur will see the martial arts movie influences from waaaay before Jackie Chan: the Shaw Brothers, some early Golden Harvest, snippets from every Venom movie ever made. There are two kinds of kung fu movies: There's the one where the hero starts off as a total badass and has to right some wrong, and the other is where he has to **become** a total badass to right some wrong. With the main character, Boon, I actually get to draw both, since he finds a ring that makes him King of Staffs, which enables him to instantly master any shaft he handles. But without a staff he's totally outclassed by everyone else in the book. So he has to learn how to handle himself without a weapon. Even though he has been given this power, the kind of skill you would normally get after years of training and sacrifice, he still has to go on the hero's journey.

It's been great working with Chuck Dixon on this. His approach so far has been designed for me to come up with the coolest thing I can possibly draw. His script is really easy to follow, and he's been leaving the look of the book entirely up to me. One of the greatest things about working with Chuck is that we speak the same language. We've seen the same films, and both of us have a long time love of the kung fu movie genre. When it came to designing Boon, all I had to do was ask Chuck which Chinese actor I thought he would look like and we both knew what was what.

CROSSGEN: Jeff, you seem to have an affinity for this material. How did you get the assignment?

JOHNSON: Actually, I wasn't the first choice for the book. Originally I was hired to be the regular relief artist at CrossGen. I don't know who they had in mind for RAT, but when I found out that CrossGen was planning a martial arts book, I practically begged to do it!

TOM RYDER: It makes sense, with your martial arts background.

JOHNSON: Yeah. I've been studying martial arts since I was a kid, and I've always wanted to draw a martial arts comic. I was a big Shang-Chi fan, particularly the Mike Zeck stuff. His run on **Master of Kung Fu** was the best. It had more power to it. More action.

The comics themselves didn't inspire me for martial arts, though. I was doing martial arts before I picked up my first comic. Then when I was about 10 or 11 I started drawing comics, doing martial arts... anything I could do to stay away from having a social life!

I started with Shitoryu, then Tae Kwon Do. The last "hard" style I studied was Sillum Fut Kung Fu, which is an abbreviated form of Shaolin Kung Fu that they taught soldiers during the Boxer Rebellion. Later I studied Aikido, which is more of a "soft" style. I hold a second degree black belt in Aikido.

CROSSGEN: And what's your style, Tom?

RYDER: Broken Pen Nib Tiger Stance.

CROSSGEN: Wow. Jeff, would you say your martial arts experience plays a big role in your art for WAY OF THE RAT?

JOHNSON: It's definitely a big factor. Even though the characters in RAT are better at their martial arts than I am, I know what they're doing. If I don't know it personally, I've seen it. Authenticity of the moves and the philosophy behind the various fighting styles is very important to me. In the martial arts, how you move reveals a lot about who you are as a person. That will certainly be true in WAY OF THE RAT.

CROSSGEN: Tom, what about you? How did you come to be teamed up with Jeff here at CrossGen?

RYDER: Well, when CrossGen contacted me I was doing storyboards out in Los Angeles, which I'd been doing for the last few years. I had been thinking about getting back into comics again when I heard about CrossGen from Tony Bedard and others. It sounded like a good place to be. I specifically came out to work with

Jeff, which was a big draw for me. I had worked with Jeff on a couple of occasions, and enjoyed it, but we never got to collaborate on anything regular. And so it seemed like the perfect job at the perfect time.

CROSSGEN: A lot of artists make the leap from comics to film and television work, but you don't often hear of artists coming back to comics.

RYDER: I did storyboards for animation, which means I translated the scripts into pictures that defined the shots. It's a lot like drawing a comic, but looser. Most of my storyboards were for animation. I worked for Sony on Jackie Chan Adventures, Starship Troopers Chronicles and Roughnecks.

I started storyboarding because it gave me a chance to draw and compose shots on my own. I got to work on some great projects at Sony, but I found I didn't have the passion for animation that I have for the medium of comics, which is my first love.

And now a seven page preview of WAY OF THE RAT, appearing next month and every month thereafter in the pages of EDGE.

"It is the wise man who can discern good fortune from ill."

Wing Tei Sun

THE FRONTIER CITY OF ZHUMAR, FAR TO THE WEST OF THE COMFORTS AND PLEASURES OF THE IMPERIAL COURT.

A FORTRESS BUILT HARD BY THE ENDLESS STEPPES.

HOME TO ONE HUNDRED THOUSAND HAPLESS SOULS WHO LIVE EACH DAY BENEATH THE SHADOW OF A TARTAR'S SWORD.

YOU'LL HAVE NO *NEED* OF THIS RING IN HELL.

NO AMOUNT OF GOLD WILL BUY YOU MERCY *THERE*.

Uh—TIGHT.

Uh?

-- AND HE HAS TOLD NO ONE OF THESE DISCOVERIES?

FATHER TRUSTS NO ONE BUT YOURSELF.

THE RING IS A SOURCE OF GREAT *WORRY* TO HIM, PRINCESS ZHENG.

IT SHOULD BE IN THE HANDS OF A *WARRIOR* NOT A SCHOLAR, TEI SU.

AND *MORE* SO THE BOOK. HE WOULD NOT TELL ME HOW HE CAME TO--

FATHER!

MURDERED. AND THE RING IS GONE.

BUT THERE IS NO MARK ON HIM. DEATH TOOK HIM WITHOUT STRUGGLE.

IT WAS NOT *DEATH* THAT TOOK YOUR FATHER, TEI.

IT WAS *FEAR*. LOOK AT HIS EYES.

Eh?

THEY HAVE GAZED INTO THE *HEART* OF HORROR.

Ai!

WHAT MIGHT HAVE FRIGHTENED HIM SO? HE WAS ALONE IN HIS LIBRARY WITH HIS BOOKS.

ALONE?

I AM NOT SO CERTAIN.

EDGE · NEXT ISSUE

CROSSGEN COMICS

Graphic Novels

THE FIRST 1	Two Houses Divided	$19.95	1-931484-04-X
THE FIRST 2	Magnificent Tension	$19.95	1-931484-17-1
MYSTIC 1	Rite of Passage	$19.95	1-931484-00-7
MYSTIC 2	The Demon Queen	$19.95	1-931484-06-6
MYSTIC 3	Seige of Scales	$15.95	1-931484-24-4
MERIDIAN 1	Flying Solo	$19.95	1-931484-03-1
MERIDIAN 2	Going to Ground	$19.95	1-931484-09-0
MERIDIAN 3	Taking the Skies	$15.95	1-931484-21-X
SCION 1	Conflict of Conscience	$19.95	1-931484-02-3
SCION 2	Blood for Blood	$19.95	1-931484-08-2
SCION 3	Divided Loyalties	$15.95	1-931484-08-2
SIGIL 1	Mark of Power	$19.95	1-931484-01-5
SIGIL 2	The Marked Man	$19.95	1-931484-07-4
SIGIL 3	The Lizard God	$19.95	1-931484-07-4
CRUX 1	Atlantis Rising	$15.95	1-931484-14-7
SOJOURN 1	From the Ashes	$19.95	1-931484-15-5
RUSE 1	Enter the Detective	$15.95	1-931484-19-8
CROSSGEN ILLUSTRATED Volume 1		$24.95	1-931484-05-8